# WHSmith

## Practice

# Problem Solving

Richard Cooper

**Age 9–11**
**Years 5–6**
Key Stage 2

# Advice for parents

The Maths *Practice* books are designed to practise and consolidate children's work in school. They are intended for children to complete on their own, but you may like to work with them for the first few pages.

- Don't let your child do too much at once. 'Little and often' is a good way to start.
- Reward your child with lots of praise and encouragement. These should be enjoyable activities for them.
- Discuss with your child what they have learned and what they can do.
- The '**Get ready**' section provides a gentle warm-up for the topic covered in the unit.
- The '**Let's practise**' section is usually the main activity. This section helps to consolidate understanding of the topic. The questions in this section get progressively harder.
- The '**Have a go**' section is often a challenge or something interesting that your child can go away and do which is related to the topic. It may require your child to use everyday objects around the home.
- The '**How have I done?**' section at the end of the book is a short informal test that should be attempted when all the units have been completed. It is useful for spotting any gaps in knowledge, which can then be revisited at a suitable moment.

- The '**Teacher's tips**' are written by practising classroom teachers. They give useful advice on specific topics or skills, to deepen your child's understanding and confidence and to help you help your child.

This book is about the 'Using and Applying' section of the curriculum, which basically means using your Maths skills to solve 'real life' problems.

By the end of Year 6 most children should be able to:

- solve multi-step problems and problems involving fractions, decimals and percentages
- suggest, plan and develop lines of enquiry
- choose and use appropriate calculation strategies at each stage, including calculator use
- understand patterns and relationships involving numbers and shapes
- tabulate systematically the information in a problem or puzzle
- identify and record steps or calculations
- explain reasoning and conclusions, using words, symbols or diagrams as appropriate.

Hachette UK's policy is to use papers that are natural, renewable and recyclable products and made from wood grown in sustainable forests. The logging and manufacturing processes are expected to conform to the environmental regulations of the country of origin.

Orders: please contact Bookpoint Ltd, 130 Milton Park, Abingdon, Oxon OX14 4SB. Telephone: (44) 01235 827720. Fax: (44) 01235 400454. Lines are open 9.00a.m.–5.00p.m., Monday to Saturday, with a 24-hour message answering service. Visit our website at www.hoddereducation.co.uk.

© Richard Cooper 2013
First published in 2007 exclusively for WHSmith by
Hodder Education
An Hachette UK Company
338 Euston Road
London NW1 3BH

This second edition first published in 2013 exclusively for WHSmith by Hodder Education.
Teacher's tips © Matt Koster 2013

Impression number     10 9 8 7 6 5 4 3
Year                             2018 2017 2016 2015 2014

This edition has been updated, 2014, to reflect National Curriculum changes.

Cover illustration by Oxford Designers and Illustrators Ltd
Character illustrations by Beehive Illustration
All other illustrations Fakenham Prepress Solutions, Fakenham, Norfolk NR21 8NN
Typeset in 16pt Folio by Fakenham Prepress Solutions, Fakenham, Norfolk NR21 8NN
Printed in Italy

A catalogue record for this title is available from the British Library.

ISBN: 978 1444 188 479

# Contents

# Welcome to Kids Club!

Hi, readers. My name's Charlie and I run Kids Club with my friend Abbie. Kids Club is an after-school club which is very similar to one somewhere near you.

We'd love you to come and join our club and see what we get up to!

I'm Abbie. Let's meet the kids who will work with you on the activities in this book.

My name's Jamelia. I look forward to Kids Club every day. The sports and games are my favourites, especially on Kids Camp in the school holidays.

Hi, I'm Megan. I've made friends with all the kids at Kids Club. I like the outings and trips we go on the best.

Hello, my name's Kim. Kids Club is a great place to chill out after school. My best friend is Alfie – he's a bit naughty but he means well!

I'm Amina. I like to do my homework at Kids Club. Charlie and Abbie are always very helpful. We're like one big happy family.

Greetings, readers, my name's Alfie! Everybody knows me here. Come and join our club; we'll have a wicked time together!

Now you've met us all, tell us something about yourself.
All the kids filled in a '**Personal Profile**' when they joined. Here's one for you to complete.

## Personal Profile

INSERT PHOTO OF YOURSELF HERE

Name: ______________________________

Age: _______

School: ____________________________

Home town: ______________________________________

Best friend: _______________________________________

My favourite:

- Book ____________________,
- Film ____________________,
- Food ____________________,
- Sport ____________________.

My hero is ____________________ because ______________

__________________________________________________________.

When I grow up I want to be a ____________________.

If I ruled the world the first thing I would do is

__________________________________________________________.

If I could be any celebrity for a day, I would be a ________

__________________________________________________________.

# 1: Place value

Place value questions often ask you to make up different numbers using different digits. The value of the digit changes depending on its 'place'.

When it's raining and we can't play outside we often play Maths card games. Knowing the values of digits helps me to win!

## Get ready

0  1  2  3  4  5  6  7  8  9

1. Kim has five digit cards. They are 7, 4, 9, 5 and 2. He can only use each card once. What is the largest three-digit number he can make? Write your answer in words. _____

2. What is the smallest three-digit number Kim can make using the cards only once? Write your answer in words. _____

3. What is the largest three-digit number Kim can make if he can use a card a maximum of two times? Write your answer in words.

_____

4. Kim swaps all his cards for five new ones. They are 1, 6, 0, 8 and 3. What is the second largest three-digit number he can make using the cards just once? Write your answer in words. _____

_____

## Let's practise

Let's make these problems a bit harder!

5  Kim now has a new set of digit cards. They are 3, 7, 4 and 8. What is the lowest four-digit number he can make using all the cards just once? Write your answer in numbers.

_____

6  Kim adds the card with the digit 5 to his hand. What is the second highest four-digit number he can make using any four of the five cards he has? Write your answer in numbers. _____

7  Kim now has all the digit cards. What is the smallest four-digit number he can make if he is allowed to use any three even digits and one odd digit? Write your answer in numbers. _____

8  Using all the cards, what is the highest four-digit number Kim can make if he uses any three odd digits and one even digit? Write your answer in numbers. _____

9  Place the digits 1, 3, 5, 7 and 9 in the boxes to get the highest answer. ☐☐ × ☐☐ + ☐ = _____

## Have a go

Play this game with a friend.

Make two sets of 0 to 9 digit cards – one for each player.

You also need a timer or a stopwatch.

Shuffle and take four cards each.

Whoever makes the largest 3-digit number in ten seconds wins the round.

The first player to win an agreed number of rounds wins the game.

### Teacher's tips

The position of a digit and its place value is the most important thing here – does the digit represent a number of units, tens, hundreds or even thousands?

# 2: Fractions

Fraction problems can be tricky because you are often dealing with words, fractions and whole numbers – lots to think about!

The Kids Club stayed in London for a weekend.

This trip to the city gave us lots of fraction problems to solve.

## Get ready

**1**  When Alfie asked the coach driver if we were 'nearly there yet' the driver replied we were halfway. At that moment, we passed a sign saying London 128 miles. How far was our journey in total?

_____

**2**  We spent three hours on a boat trip up and down the River Thames and one hour having a picnic. What fraction of the 24-hour day did we spend doing all this? _____

**3**  Charlie and Abbie booked a flight for us on the London Eye. It took 30 minutes for the Eye to go around once. One sixth of the way round I started to get frightened and wanted to get off! How long had I been on the London Eye before I got frightened?

_____

**4**  At London Zoo I counted 50 snakes in the Reptile House. Three tenths of them were poisonous, the rest weren't. How many snakes were not poisonous? _____

## Let's practise

We did a lot on our trip. Here are some more of our exploits.

**5** Jamelia spent $\frac{3}{7}$ths of her total spending money on a giant inflatable Nelson's Column from a street seller. It cost her £18 and burst after an hour! How much spending money did Jamelia bring in total? _____

**6** Kim tried to make one of the guards move who was guarding Buckingham Palace. He pulled funny faces and told his best jokes but still failed. He spent $\frac{2}{3}$ of an hour doing this while we ate ice cream. How many minutes did Kim try and make the guard move for? _____

**7** An attendant at the waxworks museum told Megan that $\frac{2}{5}$ths of their models were replaced each year. The museum had a total of 700 wax models. How many get replaced each year? _____

**8** Alfie said that $\frac{7}{10}$ths of his £30 spending money had been spent on sweets and drinks – the rest he had just wasted. How much did Alfie spend on sweets and drinks? _____

## Have a go

If you sleep on average for 8 hours a night, what fraction of your life have you spent asleep? Work out some fractions for time spent on other things you do.

### Teacher's tips

Think about what information is important in the question and what can be ignored; focus on the amounts and the actions. Write the problem down as a number sentence to help you solve it.

# 3: Decimals

Kids Club had a 'fun and games' day. It was brilliant, although Alfie is certain that someone jogged the table when he lost at Jenga. At the 'fun and games' day we had to think about some problems involving decimals.

Problems about decimals are often about measures or money. Don't forget which units you are working with.

## Get ready

1. Kim fired a pea from a pea-shooter 8.6 m. Amina fired her pea 45 cm further than Kim. How far did Amina shoot her pea? Write your answer in metres. _____

2. Jamelia fired a foam air rocket a distance of 11.8 m. I fired mine 95 cm less far. How far in metres did my rocket travel?

   _____

3. Charlie and Abbie won the three-legged race in 18.5 seconds. Alfie and Kim were 3.5 seconds behind in second place. How many seconds did it take Alfie and Kim to complete the race?

   _____

4. Jamelia held the record for completing Charlie's 50-piece jigsaw of Elvis Presley in 56.3 seconds. Amina broke the record by 7 seconds! What is the time of the new record? _____

## Let's practise

These events were great fun!

**5** Kim tossed a Wellington boot 24.78 m.
Alfie tossed his boot 22.57 m and Jamelia
tossed her wellie 4.83 m further than Alfie.
Who won and by how far? _____

**6** Amina, Kim and I played a game of 'Hoop-shoot' – the person who
scores 10 baskets with a basketball the fastest wins. Kim took 48.25
seconds. I was 5.12 seconds quicker than Kim but 3.83 seconds slower
than Amina. What was Amina's time in seconds? _____

**7** Each of us caught a snail and held a snail race. Here are the results
after 10 minutes.
Jamelia's snail travelled 19.57 cm     Alfie's snail travelled 29.17 cm
My snail travelled 18.49 cm        Amina's snail travelled 3.04 cm
Kim's snail travelled 20.73 cm

What was the difference in distance travelled between the snail that
came second and the snail that came fourth? _____

**8** All five children made a tug of war team. This is how much each of
them weighed.
Jamelia: 42.37 kg     Alfie: 41.97 kg     Amina: 36.28 kg
Kim: 40.75 kg        Megan: 37.86 kg
They tugged against Charlie and Abbie who together weighed
145.50 kg. Which was the heavier team and by how much?

## Have a go

Give yourself an imaginary £500. Look through a mail order catalogue or one
from a local store. 'Spend' the £500 on gifts for yourself and your family.
Can you spend the £500 to the exact penny?

### Teacher's tips

Convert each amount so that it is expressed the same way: if the question has
values in metres and centimetres convert the metres to centimetres first. You can
convert the answer back at the end.

# 4: Percentages

Percentage problems are sometimes about money. You might be asked to find the percentage of an amount or to work out the discount off a price.

The Kids Club have received a government grant for some new outdoor sports equipment – cool!

Charlie and Abbie took us to 'Lilly-Livers' the sports shop; there was a big sale on and we wanted to pick up some bargains.

## Get ready

1. Jamelia thought we needed a new netball post. The old one had rusted and the net had rotted years ago. One was priced at £90. It had a '10% off' tag tied to it. How much would the netball post cost after the discount? _____

2. Amina told Charlie that a set of 12 footballs would cost 15% less if you bought a carry net for £5. The set of balls was priced at £30. How much would the set of balls and a net cost altogether?

_____

3. I told the shopkeeper that because his tennis racket had lots of holes in it I wanted a 75% discount! The racket cost £40. How much did I offer to pay? _____

4. A crazy golf set cost £150, but one of the nine holes was broken and the windmill wouldn't go round, so it was on sale with 60% off. What was the price of the crazy golf set after the discount? _____

## Let's practise

These are some more great deals we got.

**5** Mountain bikes were on special offer. One was £79 with 10% off, one was £89 with 20% off and one was £99 with 30% off. Charlie and Abbie bought all three bikes. How much did they pay in total?

_____

**6** The price of a climbing frame and tyre swing was £290 in the sale. When the sale ended the price would go up by 15%. How much would it cost once the sale had ended?

_____

**7** A water-slide was on special offer because of a hose-pipe ban. You could buy one for 35% of its original price. Its price before the ban was £55. What was the price during the hose-pipe ban? _____

**8** The grant for equipment was £1300. Charlie and Abbie spent 70% in May, 10% in June and 15% in July. How much did they have left to spend when Kids Club started again in September?

## Have a go

If you put £1 in a saving account which paid 10% interest each year, how much would be in the account after 25 years? Remember to add the interest each year and then calculate the 10%. For example, after year 1 you would have £1.10. After year 2 you would have £1.21 (£1.10 plus the 10% which is 11p). Round to the nearest 1p, so for year 3 you would add 12p to make £1.33. Use a calculator to help you.

### Teacher's tips

10% is the same as $\frac{1}{10}$, which is straightforward to calculate, so calculate larger percentages by breaking them down into lots of 10%. Remember 5% will be half of whatever 10% is.

# 5: Addition

Addition problems often involve adding three- or four-digit numbers. Mistakes can be made if you are not careful. Once you have decided which calculations you need to do, remember: estimate, calculate, then check.

Charlie bought an old and broken pinball machine from a fun-fair. He repaired it and it now stands proudly in the Kids Club – we love it!

## Get ready

1   Jamelia played pinball with Alfie. Jamelia scored 487 points with her first ball, 274 with her second and the third ball went straight down the chute without scoring! How many points did Jamelia score with her three balls in total? _____

2   Alfie scored 692 with his first ball and got his score doubled when he hit the 'double trouble' bumper. His second ball scored just 25 points before he lost it between the flippers. How many points did Alfie score with the two balls in total? _____

3   Alfie did really well with his third ball. He hit lots of bumpers and targets and scored 894 points with a 977 bonus. How many points did Alfie score with his third ball in total? _____

4   How many points did Alfie and Jamelia score between them?

_____

## Let's practise

We held a pinball tournament.
Here are the final scores.

| PLAYER | FINAL SCORE |
|---|---|
| Jamelia | 5829 |
| Kim | 6728 |
| Alfie | 6092 |
| Megan | 9241 |
| Amina | 2987 |
| Charlie | 4729 |
| Abbie | 8593 |

**5** What is the total number of points scored by Charlie and Abbie?

_____

**6** What is the sum of the points for the person who came first and the person who came third? _____

**7** How many are Kim's and Jamelia's scores altogether? _____

**8** What is the total of the two lowest scores? _____

**9** How many points did the children score in total between them?

_____

## Have a go

Challenge yourself to add up totals in your head. Look for numbers around you, at home, out shopping, in newspapers and on TV. Use 'rounding' to add big numbers mentally and you'll be surprised how accurate you can be.

Practise mental addition as often as possible.

### Teacher's tips

Whichever method you choose for these calculations make sure you write down the working out in the margin or on another piece of paper. Estimate the answers by rounding the numbers; your answer should be close.

# 6: Subtraction

Subtraction problems can involve finding the difference between two-, three- or four-digit numbers. Estimating first will help you get these right. You can check your answers when you have finished.

We have been making a timeline for a display at Kids Club. When the children find out something interesting from books or from a TV programme they research it further, write a short article and mark it on the timeline. It's an on-going project.

## Get ready

1. Kim found out about the First World War which ended in 1918. How long ago was that from this year? _____

2. Jamelia was interested in the artist Vincent Van Gogh. He died in 1890. How long is it since he died? _____

3. Megan did some research on Queen Victoria. She came to the throne in 1837 and died in 1901. How long ago is 1837? _____

4. Kim studied the life and work of the composer Mozart. He was a child prodigy and was born in 1756. How many years ago is that?

   _____

## Let's practise

Alfie has written a story about travelling back in time to see exciting events in history.

Here are some of the events in the story and some questions about the dates.

**5**    Alfie travelled back to 1666 and helped to put out the Great Fire of London. How many years back is that? _____

**6**    From 1666 he then went back to join King Henry V at the Battle of Agincourt in 1415. How many years further back was that from the Great Fire of London? _____

**7**    Alfie's next adventure was leaving Agincourt to go back in time to meet the last Viking king in England, Eric Bloodaxe, in 954. How many years before Agincourt was that? _____

**8**    Alfie had heard about the beauty of the Egyptian Queen Cleopatra so in his story he travelled back to 51 BC to see for himself. How long before 954 is that? Be careful here! _____

**9**    Finally, Alfie returned to the present day but decided on one last trip in his time machine. He returned to Ancient Egypt and helped build the Great Pyramid in 2593 BC. How many years ago is that from today?

_____

## Have a go

Using books and the Internet, research five events in history which interest you.

How many years before you were born did they occur?

### Teacher's tips

Think of these timeline jumps as subtraction calculations – think about which number you need to start with and which you need to subtract from it.

# 7: Multiplication

Multiplication problems are often 'story' problems about measures or money. Make sure you identify the numbers to multiply and include the units. Remember that if you are asked to find the product of two numbers it means you must multiply them.

The children have been growing fruit and vegetables in an allotment at the back of the Kids Club. It is harvest time!

## Get ready

**1**  Jamelia has grown eight strawberry plants on the allotment. She picked 37 strawberries off each plant to make some jam. How many strawberries did Jamelia pick altogether? _____

**2**  Kim chose to grow raspberry plants. These have been very successful. From nine plants, Kim picked 45 raspberries off each one. How many raspberries did Kim pick altogether? _____

**3**  Jamelia's jam was sold to parents after school. Each pot cost £1.25. Jamelia made 20 pots. She kept three for herself and family and sold the rest. How much did she get for her jam in total? _____

**4**  Kim eventually picked 4.3 kg of raspberries. He and his Mum made 35 litres of raspberry cordial. They sold the cordial for 95p a litre after keeping 8 litres for themselves. How much did they make in total from selling the cordial? _____

## Let's practise

These are a bit more difficult but give them a go.

**5** Alfie grew potatoes and Megan grew leeks. They decided to make some leek and potato soup. It was so good; the school served it for lunch! The school paid Alfie and Megan 87p per litre. Alfie and Megan made 48 litres of soup. How much were they paid? _____

**6** Amina loves runner beans so she grew those. Each time she picked beans off the plant some more grew in their place. From 16 bean plants, Amina picked 27 beans off each one three times. How many beans did she pick altogether? _____

**7** Abbie and I both grew grapevines. From 23 vines we grew an average of 376 grapes on each. What is the number of grapes grown in total?

_____

**8** We made wine from our grapes. It was quite a good year! We managed to sell 56 bottles to a local restaurant for £1.85 per bottle. How much did the restaurant give us for the wine? _____

## Have a go

Count the number of beats your heart makes in a minute. How many times would your heart beat in an hour?

What is the product of the number of times your heart beats in an hour and the number of hours in a day? (The number of beats will vary depending on how active you are.)

### Teacher's tips

Underline the important information in the story – the quantities and the actions – and write them as numbers and maths symbols to create a number sentence with '?' as the missing information you need to calculate.

Always read division questions carefully and work out which number needs to be divided. Usually you have to find how many times the smaller number 'fits into' the bigger number.

The Kids Club support the local Premiership football team who often give cheap tickets to families, schools and clubs like ours. It can still be expensive though, so we try to save up.

## Get ready

1. There are 288 half-price tickets given equally to 12 different schools. How many tickets does each school receive? _____

2. The next allocation is for 232 tickets to the big cup match. These are given equally to eight after-school clubs like ours – hooray! How many tickets does each after-school club receive? _____

3. The football club then gives away 432 tickets for the quarter-final of the cup. They could either be shared between the 12 schools, or between the 8 after-school clubs. Who would receive more tickets, a school or an after-school club? How many more? _____

4. For the semi-final of the cup, 520 pupils, parents and children from after-school members are going. It promises to be a great day! The football club have donated a mini-bus to get people to the ground. Unfortunately, it can only take 20 people at a time for the 10-minute round trip. How long would it take to bus everyone to the ground?

_____

I'm glad I didn't hang around for the mini-bus; we all walked to the game.

**5** Twelve football-mad parents paid a total of £960 for front row seats at the match and a chance to meet the players in the players' lounge afterwards. How much did they pay equally between them? _____

**6** Sixteen other football-mad parents paid a total of £720 for autographed footballs from the players! How much did each parent pay for an autographed ball? _____

**7** The stadium can hold 45 000 people. How many mini-bus loads of 20 people is that? _____

**8** The restaurants and bars inside the stadium made £84 000. If the average amount spent by a customer was £5, how many customers used the bars and restaurants? _____

**9** The game was a sell-out and raised a total of £1 125 000 from ticket sales alone (45 000 tickets). What was the average cost of a ticket to the game? _____

## Have a go

The new Wembley Stadium can hold 90 000 people. If 50% of the seats were given to corporate hospitality, 50% of the remainder were given to season ticket holders, 50% of the remainder given to football club members and 50% of the rest given to officials and staff, how many tickets would be left to sell to the general public?

### Teacher's tips

Estimate the answer first by rounding up quantities to the nearest 10 or hundred. Read the question carefully – is it a division or multiplication problem? Highlight the key information to form the calculation. Check your answer against your estimate.

These problems involve all four operations: addition, subtraction, multiplication and division. Most of them are decimal problems as well, so watch the decimal points!

## Get ready

1. I earn £12 per week pocket money by doing jobs around the house. I want to save all my earnings for 15 weeks for when we go on holiday. How much will I have if I do save for 15 weeks? _____

2. Fifteen weeks is quite a long time without spending any money! If I save £9 per week and spend the rest, how much will I have saved after 13 weeks? _____

3. For the two weeks before our holiday I will work extra hard and deliver papers for the newsagent. I will get paid £38 for the two weeks doing the paper round.
How much will I be able to take on holiday if I take my 13 weeks' worth of savings and all my paper round earnings? _____

4. Just before we went away, I bought myself a new swimming costume with my holiday money for £19.99. My Dad gave me £10 towards it. How much of my money did I have left to spend? _____

## Let's practise

Last week I had rather a bad accident. My new scooter hit the kerb and smashed the windscreen of our neighbour's car! The damage cost £140. My Dad paid for it but I'm going to have to pay him back …

**5**    The £140 is to be paid back at a rate of £1 per day. How many weeks is that in total? _____

**6**    I can earn 25p for ironing my Dad's shirts and 35p for ironing a pair of trousers. If I iron 16 shirts and 4 pairs of trousers, how much will I still have to pay? _____

**7**    My Mum felt sorry for me. She said she would give me all the coins in her jar if I vacuumed and dusted the entire house. It was not a good deal. There were 195 pennies, 286 2p coins, 46 5p coins and 53 10p coins. How much did I collect from the jar? _____

**8**    After the ironing and cleaning, how much was left to pay of the £140?
_____

**9**    I eventually paid the money back to Dad. He was so pleased with me for working so hard, that he took me and my friends out for an Indian meal and a trip to the cinema! This is what he spent:
Tickets – £36.50     Curries and rice – £47.31     Sweets – £13.96
Popcorn – £14.28     Drinks and desserts – £27.95
How much did Dad spend in total? _____

## Have a go

Think about ways you could earn some money. Are there any jobs or errands you could do for friends and family? Add up what you could earn. Are there any unwanted toys to sell? Is there anything you want to save up for? Learning to handle money well is a useful skill.

### Teacher's tips

Money problems are just the same as other calculations because money uses the decimal system – just mind the units and decimal point to make sure you calculate the correct values.

Time problems often ask you to work out the difference between two times.

This is what I did on Saturday with Jamelia. It was her turn to sleep over at my house.

## Get ready

**1**  Jamelia called round on Saturday morning at 9.30 a.m. We left at 10.55 p.m. to catch the bus into town. How long was it from when Jamelia came round to when we left to catch the bus?

_____

**2**  We had lunch at a sandwich bar at 12.10 p.m. We were there for an hour and a half! What time did we leave the sandwich bar?

_____

**3**  We went to the cinema to see the new film which started at 2.45 p.m. It said in the magazine review that the film lasted one hour and fifty minutes, so what time did the film end? _____

**4**  My Mum picked us up after the film. Jamelia stayed the night and we were up chatting until 12.15 a.m! Dad got us out of bed in the morning at 8.45 a.m. How many hours sleep did we get? _____

# Let's practise

Jamelia and I helped my Mum and Dad cook Sunday lunch. We drew up a table for cooking times but got it all wrong and burnt the joint!

Fill in this table so the cooking times are correct.

| | KILOGRAMS/ COOKING TIMES | 1KG | 1.5KG | 2KG | 2.5KG | 3KG | 3.5KG |
|---|---|---|---|---|---|---|---|
| 5 | Roast chicken 40 mins per kilo + 20 mins | | | | | | |
| 6 | Nut roast loaf 50 mins per kilo + 25 mins | | | | | | |
| 7 | Roast pork 60 mins per kilo+ 25 mins | | | | | | |
| 8 | Frozen vegetable lasagne 80 mins per kilo + 30 mins | | | | | | |

9  If we put a 2.5 kg frozen vegetable lasagne in the oven at 10.12 a.m., at what time would it be ready? _____

# Have a go

Investigate different cooking times for different foods.

Which take longest to cook? Which ones can be cooked in seconds?

Look in recipe books and on the Internet.

Make up some Maths questions about your findings for a friend to answer.

## Teacher's tips

Remember there are 60 minutes in an hour (not 100) so even though time is written the same way as decimal numbers, you can't calculate time using the same methods.

Charlie is playing cricket for the local team. We are all going to the game to watch him. Jamelia and Kim have made a picnic and Abbie has made the tea for the players – more sandwiches and cakes than I've ever seen!

Measures problems are about adding, subtracting, dividing and multiplying weights, lengths and capacities. Lots of things to think about!

## Get ready

1   The weight of a cricket ball is 156 g. What is the weight of the six cricket balls in a box? _____

2   The width of the cricket pitch is 95 m. The umpire asks for the width to be increased by 50 cm. How wide is the pitch now in metres?

_____

3   Charlie is batting and hits the ball 36 m to score one run. The second time he hits it, the ball goes two and a half times further. How far did Charlie hit the ball on his second hit? _____

4   Charlie hits a high shot over the bowler's head. The ball travels 45 m to a fielder who fumbles the catch and knocks the ball a further 16 m. How many centimetres has the ball travelled? _____

## Let's practise

Charlie scored 56 runs! Now his team are fielding.

**5** Charlie is bowling. His run up to bowl is 15.75 m. Charlie wants to bowl faster so he increases his run up by 575 cm. How long is his run up now in metres? _____

**6** Kim lays out the picnic. He made 1.65 litres of ginger ale to share between six people. If it is shared equally, how many millilitres can each person have? _____

**7** Jamelia cooked 150 cocktail sausages. They weighed 1.5 kg. Only $\frac{3}{5}$ths were eaten. How many sausages were left and how much did they weigh? _____

**8** At the tea break, two teams of 12 players and the two umpires each eat 450 g of sandwiches and 375 g of cakes. How many kilograms of food are eaten by the players and umpires? _____

**9** After the game, the 24 players and two umpires each drink 330 ml of shandy. There is 3.5 litres of shandy left. How many litres of shandy were made altogether? _____

## Have a go

Cooking is the best way to learn about measures. Following recipes is like solving problems with measures. With the help of an adult, get an apron on and start cooking!

### Teacher's tips

Make sure you know how many centimetres are in a metre, grams in a kilogram, and millilitres in a litre before you tackle measurement problems. Write them on a sheet at home to help.

# 12: Puzzles

Today is a rainy day at Kids Club. Charlie and Abbie have set us some number puzzles to keep us busy. Have a go at them yourself.

Number puzzles can be great fun but you need to think clearly to get them right.

Solve them by taking the calculations step-by-step and picturing the numbers in your head. What are you being asked to do?

## Get ready

1 Abbie is thinking of a three-digit number. It is less than 200, can be divided exactly by 10 and the sum of the three digits is 7. What number is Abbie thinking of? _____

2 Which two numbers have a one-digit answer when multiplied and a two-digit answer when added? _____ _____

3 The ages of Gertie and Bertie add up to 55. Gertie's age is Bertie's age reversed. How old are Gertie and Bertie? _____
_____

4 There are 100 houses in Acacia Avenue. Sissy the sign-writer is ordered to number the houses from 1 to 100. How many '7s' will she need? _____

## Let's practise

These are a bit harder. Give them your best shot!

**5**   All of Charlie's underpants are red except two.
All of Charlie's underpants are blue except two.
All of his underpants are pink except two.
How many pairs of underpants does Charlie
have? _____

**6**   Megan opened her reading book and found that the sum of the facing
pages was 245. What pages did she open the book to?

_____   _____

**7**   I have three digits and I'm less than 130. I can be divided exactly by 3
and 8. What am I? _____

**8**   Amina is thinking of a three-digit number. The hundreds digit is 3 times
more than the units digit. The sum of the three digits is 4. What
number is Amina thinking of? _____

**9**   Jamelia opened her piggy bank and found she had the same number of
10p, 20p and 50p coins which totalled £25.60. How many coins did she
have in the piggy bank? _____

## Have a go

Sudoku puzzles are very popular but they are more to do with logic than
numbers. Look for some in newspapers or magazines and see if you can do
them.

### Teacher's tips

Puzzles are much easier to solve if you can translate the problem into a number
sentence. Think about the clues in the question, and focus on the quantities and
the actions.

# 13: Patterns and sequences

Pattern questions might ask you to find the 'nth' number in a pattern or to work out how many numbers are in the pattern.

We have been studying the Ancient Greeks at school. They started the Olympic Games in 776 BC but the Olympics we see today began in 1896. They happen in a pattern – every four years.

## Get ready

Fill in the missing years for these modern Olympic Games.

1    Munich 1972, Montreal 1976, Moscow _____, Los Angeles _____, Seoul 1988

2    London _____, Helsinki 1952, Melbourne 1956, Rome _____, Tokyo 1964

3    The London Olympics will be in 2012. When will the next three Olympics be held after then? _____

4    Since 1896, three Olympics have been cancelled because of war. How many games, including 1896, had there been by the end of 2004?

_____

## Let's practise

Halley's Comet is a comet that can be seen from Earth very rarely. Abbie set up a telescope to study the night sky. I wonder if she'll be able to see it?

**5** Halley's Comet was last seen in 1986. The time before, it was seen in 1910 and the time before that was 1834. Would Abbie be able to see Halley's Comet if she viewed the sky for the next 4 years? Explain your answer. _____

_____

**6** Halley's Comet appeared just before the Battle of Hastings in 1066. It was seen as an omen of doom! When were its next three appearances? _____

**7** How many appearances of Halley's Comet can we expect in the next 1000 years? _____

**8** The comet Swift–Tuttle was last seen in 1992. It will next be seen in 2127. When will the next two sightings be after that? _____

**9** The comet Denning–Fujikawa was discovered in 1881. It can be seen every nine years. It was last seen in 2007. How many times has this comet been seen since its discovery and its last appearance?

_____

## Have a go

Football is said to have been invented in Tudor times. Imagine if Elizabeth I had started the World Cup in 1588! If it was held every 8 years, how many 'World Cups' would there have been since 1588 up to the year 2000? (No breaks for wars!)

### Teacher's tips

Work out the sequence by calculating what the change is between the numbers in the sequence that you are given, then go back and apply the same change to find the missing number.

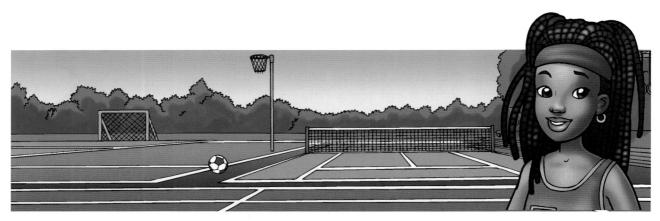

The children at Kids Club have been making and drawing shapes for a display. See if you can identify what they have drawn.

These questions might ask you to add shapes together and then work out what the new shape is. Some are quiz-type questions where you might have some clues to solve.

## Get ready

1. Megan has drawn an arrow shape. It has three sides and two of the sides are the same length. What is the name of the shape that Megan has drawn? _____

2. Alfie draws a star with six points. Each of the six points is the same distance apart. He then joins the points next to each other with straight lines. What is the name of the shape that Alfie has drawn?

   _____

3. Amina slides an equilateral triangle next to a square. The sides are lined up exactly. What is the name of the new shape? _____

4. Kim slides two equilateral triangles together so the sides are lined up exactly. What is the name of the new shape? _____

## Let's practise

These are a bit harder. Drawing them on a piece of paper might help.

**5** Charlie takes a hexagon and adds an equilateral triangle on each of the sides. The triangles fit exactly. How many sides does this new shape have? _____

**6** Abbie puts three equilateral triangles together to form a new shape; the name of it sounds like it belongs in the circus! What is the name of Abbie's shape? _____

**7** Abbie adds a fourth equilateral triangle to her new shape. Which two shapes can she make?

_____

**8** What do the prefixes 'quad', 'tri' and 'hex' stand for? _____

_____

**9** I made a beautiful flower pattern for our display. I took a regular octagon and placed a square on each of the octagon's sides. They fitted exactly. How many sides does this 'flower shape' have?

_____

## Have a go

Make sure you know all the names of the 2D shapes up to ten sides. Learn how to spell them correctly as well! If all their sides are the same length, they are 'regular polygons'. If their sides are different lengths they are 'irregular polygons'.

### Teacher's tips

As well as shape names, learn what other terms like 'equilateral' and 'right-angle' mean. To help you remember shape names think of everyday objects with the same prefixes, like tricycle, octopus and quad-bikes!

Alfie was getting a box of 3D shapes down from the cupboard. Unfortunately he stood on a stray sphere and dropped the lot! Some of the cuboids were broken.

Alfie was okay but he did hurt his bottom on a square-based pyramid – ouch!

As you should know, 3D shapes are solid shapes. It is particularly useful to be able to picture 3D shapes in your head and 'see round them'. A good imagination is useful in Maths.

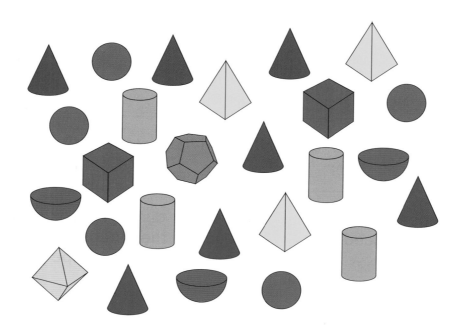

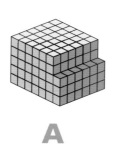

**A**

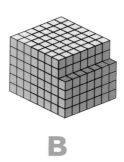

**B**

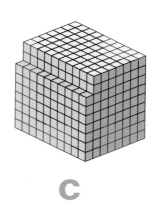

**C**

## Let's practise

Answer these questions about the pictures
on the opposite page.

**1** How many cylinders can you see?

_____

**2** How many hemispheres are there?

_____

**3** Count the number of cones. _____

**4** How many square-based pyramids are there? _____

**5** What colour is the octahedron? _____

**6** What colour is the dodecahedron? _____

**7** If the damaged shapes were repaired there would be five cubes.
True or false? _____

**8** How many blocks are needed to repair shape A so it is a complete
cuboid? _____

**9** How many blocks are needed to repair shape B so it is a complete
cuboid? _____

**10** How many blocks are needed to repair shape C so it is a complete
cuboid? _____

## Have a go

Learn all the names of the 3D shapes up to the dodecahedron and their
spellings.

It may come in useful for any tests you take.

### Teacher's tips

To help you learn 3D shape names and their properties, find objects at home that are
different shapes, or make your own, and try labelling them. Your school may have a
set you could ask your teacher to put on display.

Position and direction questions may ask you to look at maps and grid references. You may also need to find the coordinates of different landmarks.

This is a map of 'Queasy Rider' Amusement Park that is close by. It's great to visit!

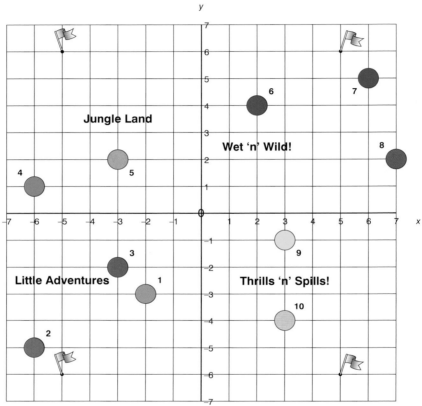

**Queasy Rider Amusement Park**

**KEY:**

| | | | | | | |
|---|---|---|---|---|---|---|
| 1 | = | Tea-Cup Ride | | 6 | = | Pirate Waterslide |
| 2 | = | Soft Play Area | | 7 | = | Log Flume |
| 3 | = | Sandpit | | 8 | = | Vertical Splash! |
| 4 | = | Big Cat World | | 9 | = | Big Hoop Coaster |
| 5 | = | Penguin Pool | | 10 | = | Queasy Rider Coaster |

= Flag

## Let's practise

1. In which zone would you find the Log Flume? _____

2. What are the coordinates of the Tea-Cup Ride? _____

3. Write down the coordinates of the Soft Play Area. _____

4. If you were at (–3, –2) where would you be? _____

5. What would you be looking at if you were at (–3, 2)? _____

6. Give the coordinates for Big Cat World. _____

7. What would you be doing at (7, 2)? _____

8. Where exactly would you find the Pirate Waterslide? _____

9. A visitor tells you the Queasy Rider is at (–4, 3). Are they correct? Explain your answer. _____

_____

10. Give the coordinates of the four Queasy Rider Flags. _____

_____

## Have a go

Sketch a map of your garden or the local park. Draw a grid and label the coordinates over the sketch in pencil. Note down the coordinates of features and landmarks in the garden or park. Write three questions you could ask a friend about your map.

### Teacher's tips

The first number is always the place on the x-axis (along/horizontal), the second is the place on the y-axis (up/vertical). Remember: across, then up.

Questions about handling data will ask you to look at a graph, chart or table and analyse the data. Sometimes you will have to transfer data from a table.

Here is a frequency chart showing how I lost at my favourite console game – 'Space Monkeys Meet the Killer Kittens'.

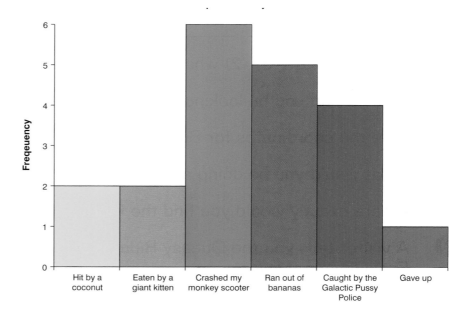

## Get ready

1. How many times did Alfie run out of bananas? _____

2. What was the most common way Alfie lost a game? _____

3. How many games in total did Alfie lose by being eaten and getting caught? _____

4. How many games did Alfie play altogether? _____

# Let's practise

As part of a Kids Club project about the history of Rock'n'Roll, we did the following survey.

'Which age group of fans think The Beatles were the most successful band ever?'

**5** Which age group of fans had the least responses?

_____

**6** Which age group answered six times in the survey?

_____

**7** How many people in the 41–50 age group said The Beatles were the most successful band? _____

**8** How many people over 30 said The Beatles were the most successful?

_____

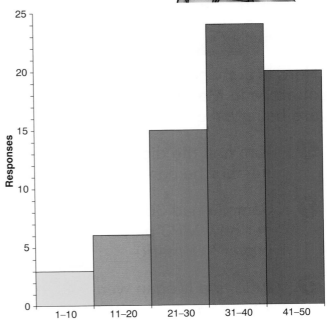

**9** How many people answered the survey altogether? _____

# Have a go

If this graph was about whether your favourite, newest band is the most successful of all time, how do you think it would look? Think about what the different age groups might say. Run the survey and draw the graph!

**Teacher's tips**

Always look very carefully at the scales on a graph; graphs that look similar can show very different data if the scales are different (you might think about when people would want to do this deliberately!).

# How have I done?

Here is a chance to see how well you are able to solve problems in a number of areas in Maths. Read the questions carefully and think about what you are being asked to do.

1   Kim has the digit cards 4, 8, 2 and 9. What is the second largest number he can make using his cards? (1 mark) _____

2   Jamelia had 360 tracks on her CDs. She put $\frac{5}{6}$ths of the tracks onto her new MP3 player. How many tracks did Jamelia put onto her MP3 player? (1 mark) _____

3   Alfie and Megan went fishing. Alfie caught a carp which was 42.8 cm long. Megan caught an eel which was 3.9 cm shorter. How long was the eel? (1 mark) _____

4   Charlie bought himself a new cricket bat in a sale. It was priced at £65 but was reduced by 20%. What was the price of the bat after the reduction? (1 mark) _____

5   Amina scored 4823 on the pinball machine and Jamelia scored 5582 more. How many points did Jamelia score in total? (1 mark) _____

6   The first manned balloon flight was in 1783. The first man to land on the Moon did so in 1969. What is the difference in years of these two aeronautical feats? (1 mark) _____

7   Abbie sold 89 homemade cakes at 75p each. How much did she make altogether? (1 mark) _____

**8**     Kim had a collection of stickers. He had 288 spares to share equally between 16 people. How many did they each receive? (1 mark)

_____

**9**     Abbie and Charlie went to a restaurant. They had 2 × lasagne at £4.85 each and 2 × fruit salad at £2.70 each. How much was the bill? (2 marks) _____

**10**     Amina read her book from 7.45 p.m. until 9.07 p.m. How many minutes did Amina read her book for? (1 mark) _____

**11**     On a sponsored walk, Alfie walked 4.8 km, Kim walked 3 km, Megan hurt her foot and walked 0.25 km, Jamelia walked 6.3 km and Amina walked 6.8 km. What was the total distance walked by all the children? (1 mark) _____

**12**     What am I? I have three digits, I am a prime number less than 200 and the sum of my digits is 14. (1 mark) _____

**13**     The first Rugby World Cup was held in 1987. It takes place every four years. When was the fifth Rugby World Cup held? (1 mark)

_____

**14**     What am I? I have three sides which are all unequal in length. (1 mark)

_____ _____

**15**     What am I? I have two faces yet I'm a 3D shape. (1 mark)

_____ _____

**16**     Charlie is facing east and makes a 270° turn clockwise. He then makes a 90° turn anti-clockwise. In which direction is he facing? (1 mark)

_____

Total marks $\frac{\phantom{00}}{17}$

## Teacher's tips

Read the questions carefully, make sure you note the units and express answers using the correct units. Make as many notes as you need in the margin or on another piece of paper. Check your work using the inverse operation.

# Maths tools

These may help you with some of the questions in this book.

| 1 WHOLE |
|---|

Fraction table showing:
- $\frac{1}{2}$, $\frac{1}{2}$
- $\frac{1}{3}$, $\frac{1}{3}$, $\frac{1}{3}$
- $\frac{1}{4}$, $\frac{1}{4}$, $\frac{1}{4}$, $\frac{1}{4}$
- $\frac{1}{5}$, $\frac{1}{5}$, $\frac{1}{5}$, $\frac{1}{5}$, $\frac{1}{5}$
- $\frac{1}{6}$, $\frac{1}{6}$, $\frac{1}{6}$, $\frac{1}{6}$, $\frac{1}{6}$, $\frac{1}{6}$
- $\frac{1}{7}$, $\frac{1}{7}$, $\frac{1}{7}$, $\frac{1}{7}$, $\frac{1}{7}$, $\frac{1}{7}$, $\frac{1}{7}$
- $\frac{1}{8}$, $\frac{1}{8}$, $\frac{1}{8}$, $\frac{1}{8}$, $\frac{1}{8}$, $\frac{1}{8}$, $\frac{1}{8}$, $\frac{1}{8}$
- $\frac{1}{9}$, $\frac{1}{9}$, $\frac{1}{9}$, $\frac{1}{9}$, $\frac{1}{9}$, $\frac{1}{9}$, $\frac{1}{9}$, $\frac{1}{9}$, $\frac{1}{9}$
- $\frac{1}{10}$, $\frac{1}{10}$, $\frac{1}{10}$, $\frac{1}{10}$, $\frac{1}{10}$, $\frac{1}{10}$, $\frac{1}{10}$, $\frac{1}{10}$, $\frac{1}{10}$, $\frac{1}{10}$

## Fraction, decimal and percentage equivalents

$\frac{1}{2} = 0.50 = 50\%$

$\frac{1}{4} = 0.25 = 25\%$

$\frac{3}{4} = 0.75 = 75\%$

$\frac{1}{10} = 0.10 = 10\%$

$\frac{1}{100} = 0.01 = 1\%$

$\frac{1}{3} = 0.333 = 33.33\%$

1 whole $= 1.0 = 100\%$ (approximately)

$\frac{1}{3} = 0.33 = 33\%$ (approximately)

$\frac{2}{3} = 0.66 = 66\%$ (approximately)

Use this hundred square to help you with your calculations.

| 1 | 2 | 3 | 4 | 5 | 6 | 7 | 8 | 9 | 10 |
|---|---|---|---|---|---|---|---|---|---|
| 11 | 12 | 13 | 14 | 15 | 16 | 17 | 18 | 19 | 20 |
| 21 | 22 | 23 | 24 | 25 | 26 | 27 | 28 | 29 | 30 |
| 31 | 32 | 33 | 34 | 35 | 36 | 37 | 38 | 39 | 40 |
| 41 | 42 | 43 | 44 | 45 | 46 | 47 | 48 | 49 | 50 |
| 51 | 52 | 53 | 54 | 55 | 56 | 57 | 58 | 59 | 60 |
| 61 | 62 | 63 | 64 | 65 | 66 | 67 | 68 | 69 | 70 |
| 71 | 72 | 73 | 74 | 75 | 76 | 77 | 78 | 79 | 80 |
| 81 | 82 | 83 | 84 | 85 | 86 | 87 | 88 | 89 | 90 |
| 91 | 92 | 93 | 94 | 95 | 96 | 97 | 98 | 99 | 100 |

# Multiplication tables

| | | | | | |
|---|---|---|---|---|---|
| 1 x 1 = 1 | 2 x 1 = 2 | 3 x 1 = 3 | 4 x 1 = 4 | 5 x 1 = 5 | 6 x 1 = 6 |
| 1 x 2 = 2 | 2 x 2 = 4 | 3 x 2 = 6 | 4 x 2 = 8 | 5 x 2 = 10 | 6 x 2 = 12 |
| 1 x 3 = 3 | 2 x 3 = 6 | 3 x 3 = 9 | 4 x 3 = 12 | 5 x 3 = 15 | 6 x 3 = 18 |
| 1 x 4 = 4 | 2 x 4 = 8 | 3 x 4 = 12 | 4 x 4 = 16 | 5 x 4 = 20 | 6 x 4 = 24 |
| 1 x 5 = 5 | 2 x 5 = 10 | 3 x 5 = 15 | 4 x 5 = 20 | 5 x 5 = 25 | 6 x 5 = 30 |
| 1 x 6 = 6 | 2 x 6 = 12 | 3 x 6 = 18 | 4 x 6 = 24 | 5 x 6 = 30 | 6 x 6 = 36 |
| 1 x 7 = 7 | 2 x 7 = 14 | 3 x 7 = 21 | 4 x 7 = 28 | 5 x 7 = 35 | 6 x 7 = 42 |
| 1 x 8 = 8 | 2 x 8 = 16 | 3 x 8 = 24 | 4 x 8 = 32 | 5 x 8 = 40 | 6 x 8 = 48 |
| 1 x 9 = 9 | 2 x 9 = 18 | 3 x 9 = 27 | 4 x 9 = 36 | 5 x 9 = 45 | 6 x 9 = 54 |
| 1 x 10 = 10 | 2 x 10 = 20 | 3 x 10 = 30 | 4 x 10 = 40 | 5 x 10 = 50 | 6 x 10 = 60 |
| 1 x 11 = 11 | 2 x 11 = 22 | 3 x 11 = 33 | 4 x 11 = 44 | 5 x 11 = 55 | 6 x 11 = 66 |
| 1 x 12 = 12 | 2 x 12 = 24 | 3 x 12 = 36 | 4 x 12 = 48 | 5 x 12 = 60 | 6 x 12 = 72 |

| | | | | | |
|---|---|---|---|---|---|
| 7 x 1 = 7 | 8 x 1 = 8 | 9 x 1 = 9 | 10 x 1 = 10 | 11 x 1 = 11 | 12 x 1 = 12 |
| 7 x 2 = 14 | 8 x 2 = 16 | 9 x 2 = 18 | 10 x 2 = 20 | 11 x 2 = 22 | 12 x 2 = 24 |
| 7 x 3 = 21 | 8 x 3 = 24 | 9 x 3 = 27 | 10 x 3 = 30 | 11 x 3 = 33 | 12 x 3 = 36 |
| 7 x 4 = 28 | 8 x 4 = 32 | 9 x 4 = 36 | 10 x 4 = 40 | 11 x 4 = 44 | 12 x 4 = 48 |
| 7 x 5 = 35 | 8 x 5 = 40 | 9 x 5 = 45 | 10 x 5 = 50 | 11 x 5 = 55 | 12 x 5 = 60 |
| 7 x 6 = 42 | 8 x 6 = 48 | 9 x 6 = 54 | 10 x 6 = 60 | 11 x 6 = 66 | 12 x 6 = 72 |
| 7 x 7 = 49 | 8 x 7 = 56 | 9 x 7 = 63 | 10 x 7 = 70 | 11 x 7 = 77 | 12 x 7 = 84 |
| 7 x 8 = 56 | 8 x 8 = 64 | 9 x 8 = 72 | 10 x 8 = 80 | 11 x 8 = 88 | 12 x 8 = 96 |
| 7 x 9 = 63 | 8 x 9 = 72 | 9 x 9 = 81 | 10 x 9 = 90 | 11 x 9 = 99 | 12 x 9 = 108 |
| 7 x 10 = 70 | 8 x 10 = 80 | 9 x 10 = 90 | 10 x 10 = 100 | 11 x 10 = 110 | 12 x 10 = 120 |
| 7 x 11 = 77 | 8 x 11 = 88 | 9 x 11 = 99 | 10 x 11 = 110 | 11 x 11 = 121 | 12 x 11 = 132 |
| 7 x 12 = 84 | 8 x 12 = 96 | 9 x 12 = 108 | 10 x 12 = 120 | 11 x 12 = 132 | 12 x 12 = 144 |

# Number line from –20 to +20

-20    -10    0    10    20

# Glossary

These are words you may come across when problem solving at home or at school. Many Maths questions come in the form of 'word problems' so it's really important that you understand what you are being asked to do! Always read the question and then read it again to help your understanding. When you arrive at an answer, does it look sensible? If not, re-read the question and check your calculations.

**Answer** – The solution to a problem. Usually what you are trying to find out!

**Calculate** – To 'work out' mathematically.

**Calculation** – If you are asked to 'show your calculations' then write down the 'working out' that you did to get your answer.

**Correct** – The right answer; or you can correct your mistakes by changing wrong answers to right ones.

**Equation** – A statement that shows two mathematical expressions are equal. (Using the sign =) For example, $10 + 5 = 15$.

**Jotting** – Brief or short notes that you might make in your book or on paper.

**Mental calculation** – 'Working out' that you do in your head. When solving problems you should first try to do them in your head. If they are too hard, use a written method. If they are still too hard then use a calculator.

**Method** – A way of doing something. You may be asked to 'explain your method'. This means write down how you tackled the problem.

**Number sentence** – E.g. $46 - 32 = 14$ is a number sentence. So is $(5 \times 3) + 69 - 11 = 73$.

**Operation** – The four operations you need to know are addition, subtraction, multiplication and division. You may be asked 'Which operation did you use?'

**Symbol** – Maths uses lots of symbols. $+$, $-$, x and $\div$ are the symbols for the four operations. Others are $=$ for equals, $>$ for greater than and $<$ for less than.

## Strategies for Solving Problems

**At the beginning –**

- How are you going to tackle the problem?
- What information do you have?
- Will you need any equipment?
- What method are you going to use?
- Can you predict or estimate the answer?

**During the problem –**

- Can you explain to yourself what you have done so far?
- Could there be a quicker way to do this?
- Can you see a pattern or a rule?
- Is there another method that would have worked?
- How will you show your results?

**Stuck? –**

- What did you do last time? What is different this time?
- Is there something you already know that might help?
- Can you put things in order?
- Would drawing a picture/graph/table/diagram help?
- Have you worked through the problem step-by-step in a logical way?

**Problem solved! –**

- How did you get your answer?
- Have you checked your answer?
- Does your answer make sense?
- If you were doing it again, what would you do differently?
- What have you learned or found out today?

# Answers

## Unit 1 (pages 6 and 7)
1 Nine hundred and seventy-five
2 Two hundred and forty-five
3 Nine hundred and ninety-seven
4 Eight hundred and sixty-one
5 3478
6 8753
7 1246
8 9875
9 $93 \times 75 + 1 = 6976$

## Unit 2 (pages 8 and 9)
1 256 miles
2 $\frac{4}{24} = \frac{1}{6}$
3 5 minutes
4 35
5 £42
6 40 minutes
7 280
8 £21
Have a go: $\frac{1}{3}$

## Unit 3 (pages 10 and 11)
1 9.05 m
2 10.85 m
3 22 seconds
4 49.3 seconds
5 Jamelia, by 2.62 m
6 39.3 seconds
7 2.24 cm
8 The children, by 53.73 kg

## Unit 4 (pages 12 and 13)
1 £81
2 £30.50
3 £10
4 £60
5 £211.60
6 £333.50
7 £19.25
8 £65
Have a go: £10.92

## Unit 5 (pages 14 and 15)
1 761
2 1409
3 1871
4 4041
5 13 322
6 15 969
7 12 557
8 7716
9 30 877 (Don't count Charlie and Abbie!)

## Unit 6 (pages 16 and 17)
(Answers relevant to 2007)
1 89 years
2 117 years
3 170 years
4 251 years
5 341 years
6 251 years
7 461 years
8 1005 years
9 4600 years

## Unit 7 (pages 18 and 19)
1 296
2 405
3 £21.25
4 £25.65
5 £41.76
6 1296
7 8648
8 £103.60

## Unit 8 (pages 20 and 21)

1 24
2 29
3 $432 \div 12 = 36$, $432 \div 8 = 54$. A club would receive 18 tickets more than school.
4 4 hours 20 minutes
5 £80
6 £45
7 2250
8 16 800
9 £25
Have a go: 5625

## Unit 9 (pages 22 and 23)

1 £180
2 £117
3 £155
4 £145.01
5 20 weeks
6 £134.60
7 £15.27
8 £119.33
9 £140

## Unit 10 (pages 24 and 25)

1 1 hour 25 minutes
2 1.40 p.m.
3 4.35 p.m.
4 $8 \frac{1}{2}$ hours
5 Chicken: 1 hour, 1 hour 20 min, 1 hour 40 min, 2 hours, 2 hours 20 min, 2 hours 40 min
6 Nut roast: 1 hour 15 min, 1 hour 40 min, 2 hours 5 min, 2 hours 30 min, 2 hours 55 min, 3 hours 20 min
7 Pork: 1 hour 25 min, 1 hour 55 min, 2 hours 25 min, 2 hours 55 min, 3 hours 25 min, 3 hours 55 min
8 Frozen vegetable lasagne: 1 hour 50 min, 2 hours 30 min, 3 hours 10 min, 3 hours 50 min, 4 hours 30 min, 5 hours 10 min
9 2.02 p.m.

## Unit 11 (pages 26 and 27)

1 936 g
2 95.5 m
3 90 m
4 6100 cm
5 21.5 m
6 275 ml
7 60 sausages, weighing 600 g
8 21.45 kg
9 12.08 l

## Unit 12 (pages 28 and 29)

1 160
2 9 and 1
3 32 and 23; or 41 and 14
4 20
5 3 pairs
6 122 and 123
7 120
8 301
9 96 coins: $32 \times 50p$, $32 \times 20p$, $32 \times 10p$

## Unit 13 (pages 30 and 31)

1 Moscow 1980, Los Angeles 1984
2 London 1948, Rome 1960
3 2016, 2020, 2024
4 25
5 No, because it only appears every 76 years.
6 1142, 1218 and 1294
7 13
8 2262 and 2397
9 15
Have a go: 51 World Cups

## Unit 14 (pages 32 and 33)
1 Isosceles triangle
2 Hexagon
3 Irregular pentagon
4 Rhombus
5 12
6 Trapezium
7 Equilateral triangle and parallelogram (or an irregular hexagon)
8 Four, three and six
9 24

## Unit 15 (pages 34 and 35)
1 4
2 3
3 7
4 3
5 Pink
6 Green
7 False
8 12
9 14
10 20

## Unit 16 (pages 36 and 37)
1 Wet 'n' Wild!
2 (–2, –3)
3 (–6, –5)
4 Sandpit
5 Penguins
6 (–6, 1)
7 Vertical Splash!
8 (2, 4)
9 No, the Queasy Rider is at (3, –4)
10 (–5, –6), (–5, 6), (5, 6), (5, –6)

## Unit 17 (pages 38 and 39)
1 5
2 Crashing his monkey scooter
3 6
4 20
5 1 to 10
6 11 to 20
7 20
8 44
9 68

## How have I done? (pages 40 and 41)
1 9824
2 300
3 38.9 cm
4 £52
5 10 405
6 186 years
7 £66.75
8 18
9 £15.10
10 82 minutes
11 21.15 km
12 167 or 149
13 2003
14 Scalene triangle
15 Hemisphere or cone
16 West